The Vowel Street Party

Written by Stephanie Laslett
Illustrated by Jane Launchbury

Collins

An imprint of HarperCollins*Publishers*

Letterland is a very friendly land, and one of the friendliest places there is Vowel Street. This is where the Vowel Men, Mr A, Mr E, Mr I, Mr O and Mr U and their families live.

One sunny day Mr E was in his garden. "Before I can plant my seeds I must pull out all these weeds," he said. He pulled and pulled, but the weeds were too strong.

Just then a voice said, "You need a spade!" It was Mr A. With his help the job was soon done.
"Time to take it easy," said Mr E as they both sat down on Mr E's garden seat.

Easygrow
Seeds

From their seat they could see the rest of Vowel Street.
Mr and Mrs I were admiring their new front door light.
It came on by itself at night, and shone very white and bright.

Mr and Mrs O were both opening the windows of their dome home to let in all the sunshine.

They could even hear Mr U playing the flute in his Music Room — as usual!

The two Vowel Men agreed that Vowel Street was a very nice place to live.

"We should have a party," said Mr A.
"A **Street** Party!" agreed Mr E.

D.I.Y.
MANUAL

Next door Mrs I heard them talking. "What a good idea," she cried. Soon the five Vowel families had everything planned. Mr O and his wife put up notices all over Letterland so everyone would know where to go.

On the day of the party the sun shone bright and clear. Mr and Mrs A and their children set out tables all the way down Vowel Street. Mr E and Mr A brought the tea. Mr and Mrs I provided ice creams and old Mr and Mrs O sold hot baked potatoes.

"My family and I will play some music," said Mr U.
Soon Vowel Street was full of people having a lovely time.

Ice Creams
Hot Potatoes
Tea

Mr U and his family were about to begin their concert. Mrs U had glued a notice to the Music Room door.

The Vowel Street Party Concert
Instruments:
Flute, lute and ukuleles

The whole family were dressed in smart blue uniforms. Mr U played some jolly tunes on his flute. Mrs U played the lute and their two children played their ukuleles.

Even Vase of Violets joined in, playing some tiny violins. In the corner Poor Peter played the piano.

Unusual Tunes

On top of Mr O's stall was a large yellow arrow.
"Just follow the arrow," called Mr O. "Tasty baked potatoes just ready to go."

Along came Jumping Jim.
"Hello, young fellow!" cried Mr O.
"Would you like a potato or two?"

"I'll have six potatoes, please," replied Jumping Jim.

"Six! I hope you won't eat them all in one go," joked Mr O.

Hot
Potatoes

But Jumping Jim didn't want to eat them at all. Can you guess what he did instead?
He juggled with them, of course!

"Ho, ho, ho," laughed Mr O. "See those potatoes go."
But then Jim started to jump as well as juggle.

"Help! They are just a bit too hot," he shouted. "Look out!"
The potatoes fell from Jim's hands and landed, *SPLAT*, all over the ground.
"Oh, no," said Mr O. So Mrs O posted up a notice while Jumping Jim cleared up the mess.

Further up the street Mr and Mrs I were selling all kinds of ice cream.
"Nice ice cream! I like it, you like it, everybody likes it!" they cried.
There was a sign behind the stall.

Private
Ice supplies

"Five fine ices for me, please," said Fireman Fred.

Quarrelsome Queen was next in line but she couldn't find an ice cream that she liked.

"Why not try mine?" said Mrs I.
"Take a bite. You might like it."
But Quarrelsome Queen didn't.
"Never mind," smiled Mrs I.

Ice Creams
Private
Ice
Supplies

Mr E was performing easy magic tricks for everyone to see.

First he took Max's **cap**. With a flash of magic sparks he turned it into a brand new **cape** for Kicking King.

Then he took a tiny little **pin**, and turned it into a big **pine** tree!

Then he took an old **tub**, and turned it into a shining new **tube**.
"But I was going to plant flowers in that **tub**," cried Ticking Tess.

"Don't worry," said Mr E. "I'll take away my magic."
Suddenly the **tube** became a **tub** again!

Near by Mr and Mrs A were selling toffee apples on a large plate.

"Tasty toffee apples to take away!" shouted Mr A. "Don't delay. Pay today!"

Hundreds of apples were packed in crates. A big pan of toffee was bubbling away. But Mr A was so busy that he didn't see the toffee bubbling up and out of the pan. Soon there was sticky toffee all over the street. Mr A looked at the mess in dismay. He put up a sign.

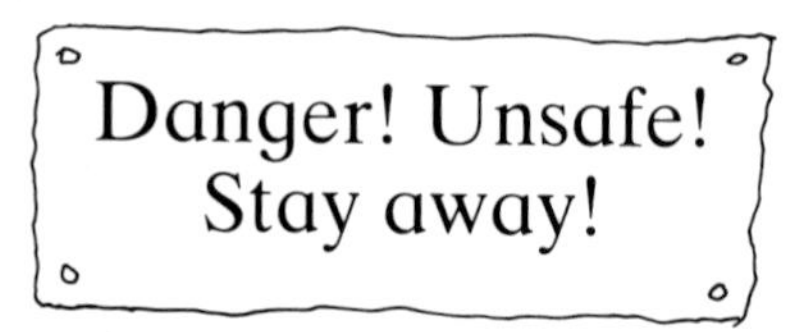

"No more toffee apples today," said Mrs A.

By now the food was ready on the tables. It was time for the party to really begin.

"Don't race!" called Mrs A. "There's lots of space."
But just as everyone sat down …
pitter-patter-pitter-pat. Wet spots appeared right across the tablecloth.
It was raining!

"Rain, rain, go away. Come again another day," cried Mr A.
"Oh, no. What a blow!" moaned Mr O.
"The sunshine was so fine," sighed Mr and Mrs I.
"We can't eat in a wet Vowel Street," said Mr E.

Suddenly, out from the Music Room rushed Mr U. In his arms he had hundreds of umbrellas.
"Mr U to the rescue!" he cried.
"Bravo!" called Mr O.

Everyone helped to open the umbrellas. And because they were Letterland umbrellas they hovered over the long line of tables, keeping everyone snug and dry. Somehow the food tasted especially good after that.

Mr U looked happy. He loved being useful.
"What a hero!" shouted Mr O.
"Hip, hip, hooray!" exclaimed Mr A.
"Never let rain spoil your day!"

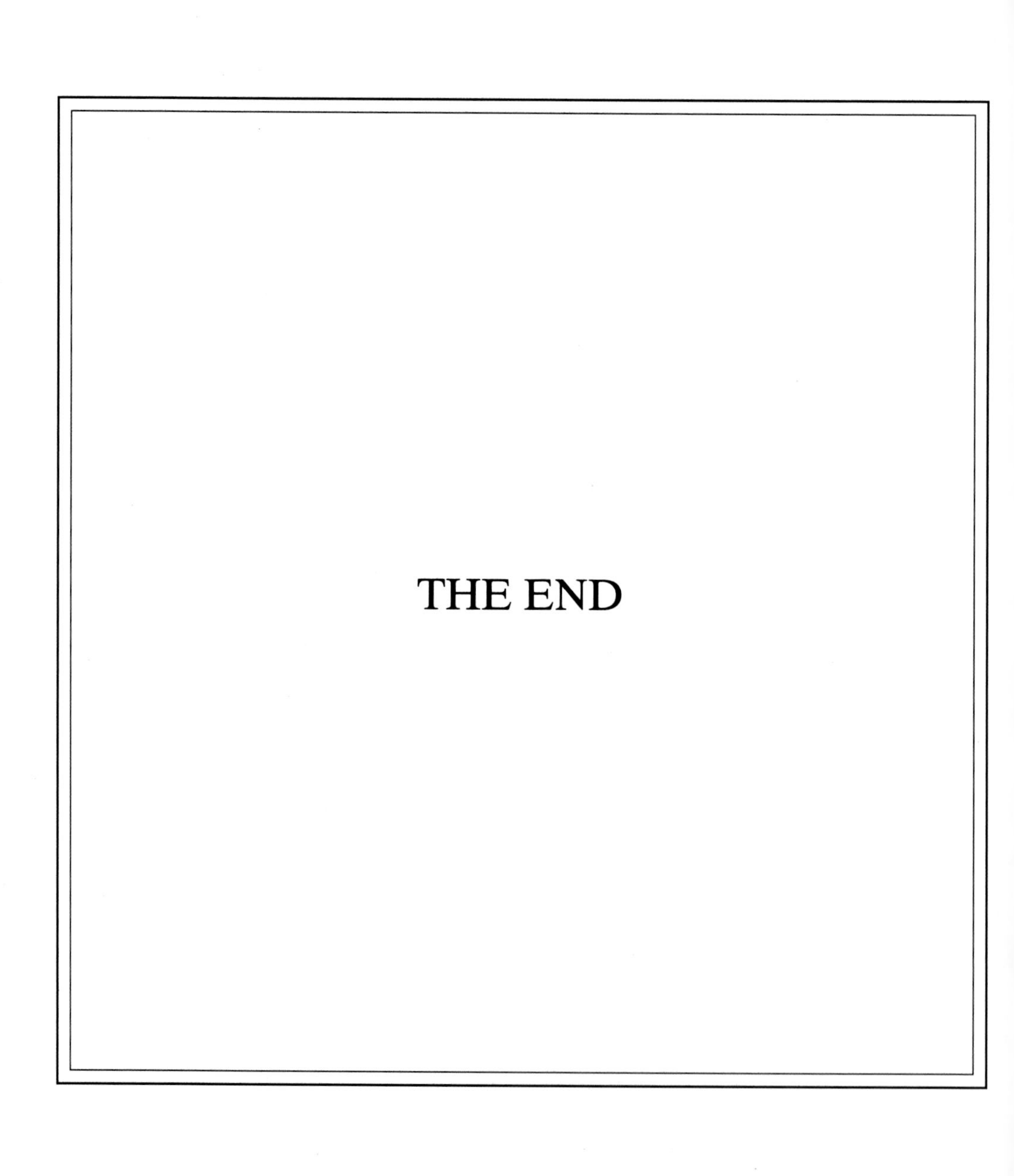
THE END